# Zoom In

**Advisory Panel**

Cathy Bogusat
Christine Finochio
Mary Francone
Helen Hohmann
Jan McDonald
John McLaughlin
Sharon McPhail
Fiona Morrison
Mary Nall
Lorraine Prokopchuk

## Senior Program Consultant

Jennette MacKenzie

## Senior Consultants

Sharon Siamon
Frieda Wishinsky

 I(T)P Nelson

*an International Thomson Publishing company*

Toronto • Albany • Bonn • Boston • Cincinnati • Detroit • London • Madrid • Melbourne
Mexico City • New York • Pacific Grove • Paris • San Francisco • Singapore • Tokyo • Washington

**I(T)P®** International Thomson Publishing

The ITP logo is a trademark under licence
www.thomson.com

© Copyright ITP®Nelson, 1999

Published by
I(T)P® Nelson

A division of Thomson Canada Limited
1120 Birchmount Road
Scarborough, Ontario  M1K 5G4
www.nelson.com

Printed and bound in Canada
2 3 4 5 6 7 8 9 0/ML/7 6 5 4 3 2 1 0 9 8

**Canadian Cataloguing in Publication Data**
Main entry under title:
Nelson language arts, [levels A-E]
For use in kindergarten and grade 1.
Contents: Level A. Jump in — Level B. Swing in — Level C. Slide in — Level D. Zoom in — Level E. Dive in.
ISBN 0-17-618544-5 (level A)    ISBN 0-17-618545-3 (level B)
ISBN 0-17-618546-1 (level C)    ISBN 0-17-618547-X (level D)
ISBN 0-17-618548-8 (level E)

1. Readers (Primary). I. Siamon, Sharon. II. Wishinsky, Frieda

PE1119.N44 1998                 428.6               C98-930370-5

**Publisher:** Mark Cobham
**Executive Editor:** Susan Green
**Production Coordinator:** Theresa Thomas
**Marketing Manager:** Mark Cressman
**Art Direction and Design:** Sylvia Vander Schee and Peggy Rhodes
**Cover Illustration:** Amy Wummer and Lindsay Grater

# Table of Contents

# At Bat

by Frieda Wishinsky

It's my first time at bat.
My knees shake.

Anne pitches.
I swing.
I miss.
"Strike one!"

Anne is ready.
My knees shake.
Anne pitches.
I swing.
I miss.
"Strike two!"

Anne is ready.
My stomach hurts.
Anne pitches.
I swing.
I hit!

The ball flies up and down.

I run fast.
I am safe at first base.
My knees don't shake.
My stomach doesn't hurt.

I'm a baseball player!

# A Baby Elephant's Trunk

by Sharon Siamon

Baby elephants are small.
But they grow fast!

Baby elephants eat a lot of food.
They eat leaves and grass.

They pick the leaves with their trunks.
They use their trunks to eat.

Baby elephants also use their trunks
to drink.

Sometimes, they use their trunks
to take baths.

Baby elephants stay close to their mothers.
They hold on with their trunks.

Baby elephants use their trunks
for eating, drinking, and holding
on to each other.

An elephant's trunk is really its nose.
How would you like to have a nose like that?

# The Elephant

## Traditional

An elephant goes like this and that.
He's terribly big and he's terribly fat.
He has no fingers, he has no toes,
But goodness, gracious,
What a nose!

# How to Draw an Elephant

1. Draw a rectangle for the body.

2. Draw a small rectangle for the head.

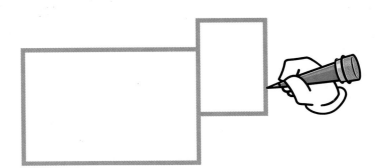

## 3. Draw four rectangles for legs.

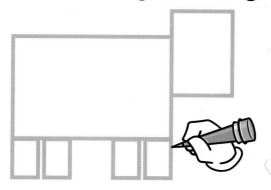

## 4. Draw a circle for the ear.

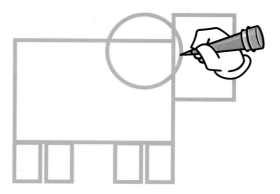

## 5. Draw a trunk and a tail. Add an eye.

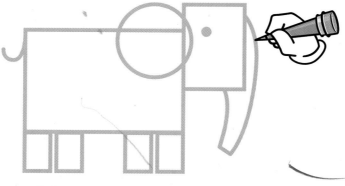

## Look! Your elephant's done!

# Dear Max

by Sharon Siamon

We saw Max on TV.
We loved his CD.
"Let's call him today.
What can we say?"

We called on the phone.
But Max wasn't home.
We left him a message.

"Hi Max. You are cool.
Please come to our school."

We had no reply.
We gave e-mail a try.

We sent a note.

Dear Max,
You are cool.
Please come to our school.

Max still didn't call.
"He's too busy, that's all.
He could be on tour.
We just can't be sure."

One day out for gym,
a big bus drove in.
"It's Max! Max is here!"
We all gave a cheer.

"Kids, thanks for your call.
Thanks for your note.
I was happy to read
the message you wrote."

"I'm glad I could come.
Here's a song just for fun.
It's for all of you kids
in Miss Capek's Grade One."

# Family Picture

by Pauline Cartwright

Mom and Dad are at the back.
Ravi and I will be in front.
Where is Ravi?

Ravi is behind Dad.

Mom and Dad are at the back.
Ravi and I will be in front.
Where is Ravi?

Ravi is between the chairs.

Mom and Dad are at the back.
Ravi and I will be in front.
Where is Ravi?

Ravi is under the table.

Mom and Dad are at the back.
Ravi and I will be in front.
Where is Ravi?

Ravi is by the door.

Mom and Dad are at the back.
Ravi and I will be in front.
Where is Ravi?

Ravi has gone!

Mom and Dad are at the back.
Ravi and I will be in front.
Where is Ravi?

Ravi is beside me.

Quick! Take the picture!

# Media Mix

# Let's Feed the Birds

## by Amy Treleaven

Leah looked outside. Oh no!
The bird feeder was full of snow.

Leah put on her snowsuit.
Leah put on her mitts and hat.
Leah put on her hood and scarf.

Leah put on her big yellow boots.

She put bird seed in her pockets.

Leah said, "Come on, George.
Let's feed the birds."

George didn't need a snowsuit.
George didn't need a hood or scarf.

George was wearing a great big fur coat!

Leah and George jumped in the snow.
George made great big dog prints.
Leah made great big girl prints.

George ran in big snowy circles.
Leah ran in big snowy circles.

George rolled in the soft fluffy snow.
Leah made snow angels.

Leah jumped into the snowbank.
George jumped into the snowbank, too!

Leah and George looked like
two big white snowballs.

"George!" said Leah.
"We forgot to feed the birds!"

Leah looked in her pockets.
She had no more bird seed.
She said, "Let's go in, George.
My hands are cold."

Leah looked out the window.
"Hey," she said.
"We **did** feed the birds!"

"Woof," said George.

# First Snow

by Marie Louise Allen

Snow makes whiteness where it falls.
The bushes look like popcorn balls.
And places where I always play,
Look like somewhere else today.

# The Guessing Jar

adapted by Susan Green

Mrs. Doran is our teacher.
On Tuesday, she held up
a big jar. It had lots of string
inside it.

"We are going to guess how long
the string is," she said.

On Thursday, she asked us who
would like to take the jar home.
We all put our hands up, but
Mrs. Doran picked me.

On Friday, I put the jar on the
kitchen table. I looked at it
and thought, "How long is
the string?"

I looked and looked. There was
a lot of tape around the top
of the jar.

I looked some more.
I took off the tape.
It went round and round and round.

I took off the lid.
I took out the string.
I measured it.

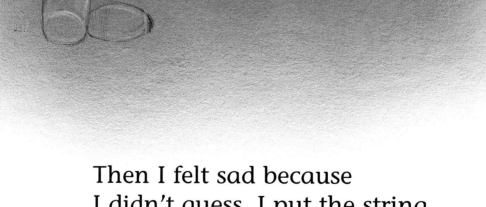

Then I felt sad because
I didn't guess. I put the string
back in the jar. I put the lid on.
I put new tape around it.

Mom came in.

"Did you measure the string, Gabe?"

"Yes. I wanted to know how long it was."

"Gabe. You'll have to tell Mrs. Doran."

"I know, Mom."

On Monday, I waited for Mrs. Doran
to be alone. Then I told her.
I thought she would be mad, but
she wasn't. She smiled and said,
"Thank you for telling me, Gabe."

"Now you can guess how many paper clips are in the jar."

"No thank you. Someone else can guess **this** time."

**Acknowledgments**

"A Baby Elephant's Trunk" and "Dear Max" copyright © Sharon Siamon, 1998; "At Bat" copyright © Frieda Wishinsky, 1998; "Family Picture" text copyright © Pauline Cartwright, 1994. Published by Nelson Australia Pty Ltd in 1994 as "Taking Our Photo". Reprinted with permission. "Let's Feed the Birds" copyright © Amy Treleaven; "First Snow" by Marie Louise Howarth. Used by permission of HarperCollins Publishers. "The Guessing Jar" adapted from "How Long Is a Piece of String" by Kirsten Atkins, text copyright © Kirsten Atkins, 1994. Published by Nelson Australia Pty Ltd in 1994. Adapted with permission.

**Illustrations**

Toni Goffe, pp.4-10, pp.22-29; Graham Percy, p.19; Ian Greener, pp.20-21; Caroline Merola, pp.30-36; Scot Ritchie, pp.37-39; Sami Suomalainen, p.52; Stephen Taylor, pp. 53-63.

**Photographs**

Mitsuaki Iwago/Minden Pictures, pp.11, 13; Jean Sioman/Valan Photos, p.12; Frans Lanting/Minden Pictures, p.14; Joe MacDonald/Visuals Unlimited, p.15; A.D. Copley/Visuals Unlimited, p.16; Glen Oliver/Visuals Unlimited, p.17; Pam E. Hickman/Valan Photos, p.18; Cydney Conger/First Light, p.37; Comstock Stock Photography, p.38; Rommel/Masterfile, p.39.